To Cliff

A MESSAGE TO THE PARENT–

As a caring parent, you want your child to be a healthy, secure and honest person. And you know that this will happen only if you yourself are a model of these qualities. You realize that your child can mature into a responsive adult only if his or her curiosity is encouraged; and youthful questions are answered with unbiased and factual explanations. So when your child asks – "Where do I come from?" – it is your responsibility to help him or her understand the wonderment of the body, and the functions that human beings – and animals – possess as males and females. This responsibility can't be escaped – for whatever the answer, it is bound to leave a lasting impression.

Here is a book that helps you explain the facts to your child without being shocking. It gently answers the questions your child asks.

Let us set examples today which will leave a healthy impression for generations to come.

Donald Sloan, M.D.
Director. Division of Sex Education
Dept. of Obstetrics and Gynecology
New York Medical College

Published by Platt & Munk Publishers, New York.
All rights reserved. No portion of this book may be reproduced without written permission of the publisher.

Printed in Belgium by Offset-Printing Van den Bossche

Library of Congress Catalog Card Number 73-19468

ISBN: 0-8228-7120-3

"Mommy, Where Do Babies Come From?"

By Simone Zapun
Illustrated by Tina Cacciola

Platt & Munk, Publishers/New York

This mud castle would make a lovely home for a squirrel,
Laura thought as she patted it. Suddenly, she heard thumping
footsteps. Her friend, Sammy, was marching toward her. His
freckled face was screwed up, his jaw was set, he was in a hurry.
"I'm on a search to find out where babies come from," he said.
"How come?" she asked.

"Because my mommy's going to have one and I want to know where it's coming from. After all, I'll have to share everything with it. My toys, my room, even my mommy and daddy."

"Gee Sammy, I always thought it would be fun to have a baby sister or brother. That way I'd never be alone."

"I'm never alone as it is. Somebody's always snooping around. Anyway, I'm going now. Do you want to come along?"

"Okay," Laura answered, and the two children started out.

They climbed up a rocky hill and came to a garden. Baby buds were in it. So was a sign: DOCTOR BEN'S FLOWER NURSERY.

Laura wondered aloud, "When baby people are born, they stay in nurseries just like these buds. Maybe people and flowers come from the same place."

"Let's find out!" Sammy cried and entered the garden. He saw Doctor Ben, and said eagerly, "We're on a search to find out where babies come from. Could you tell us about buds?"

"Of course I can," Doctor Ben replied, because he loved flowers and children, too. "But you must listen carefully."

"Every flower is part of a plant, and every baby plant comes from a grown plant. At first, the plant is a tiny egg that looks like a dot. It lies in the ovary of a grown flower. The ovary is where the stem and petals meet.

"The egg cannot become a plant all by itself. It must join with pollen. Sometimes, bees help the egg and the pollen join.

"As bees fly around, they collect grains of pollen from the flowers and put them into baskets which grow on the backs of their legs. As some grains fall in the baskets, others fall out and land on flower petals, near the ovary.

"One grain grows into the ovary and joins with the egg. It changes the egg into a seed. This is called fertilization, and it means that the egg now can grow into a plant.

"The seed drops out of the flower into the earth. With the sunshine and the rain, it grows into a plant. It looks just like the plant it fell out of.

"And that's how a baby flower is born. Do you understand?"

"I think so," Sammy answered. "But . . .

"Do bees help make people babies too? Did my mommy get stung?"

"No," answered Doctor Ben. "But eggs are inside your mommy, just like they are inside a flower."

"Then why doesn't she have a flower instead of a baby?"

"Because flower eggs can only make flower babies and people eggs can only make people babies."

"That doesn't seem fair," Sammy said, tapping his foot.

"Maybe not, but that's how nature works. You might get a better idea if you look at birds' eggs. When birds have babies, they lay fertilized eggs in nests. A shell covers them to protect them. Up the hill, in a blue house, lives a lady who takes care of birds. She can tell you how they are born.

"Her name is Miss Florence. Go and ask her."

The children said thank you and went on.

"If baby buds look just like the flowers they come from, how come I don't look just like my mommy. I'm not even a girl," Sammy wondered.

"Maybe your mommy didn't make you all by herself. After all, the egg didn't grow into a plant all by itself."

"Hmmm. Maybe not."

They came to a sky-blue house. A lady with a bright kerchief wrapped around her hair was standing in front of it. As soon as she saw the children, she smiled.

Sammy marched up to her.

"We are on a search to find out where babies come from. Doctor Ben said that you could tell us where bird babies come from. Could you?" He said, all in one breath.

"I think so," she smiled and led them inside.

As Miss Florence lifted two birds on her arm, the children saw that her rooms were filled with hay and seeds and nests.

Then she said, "This is a mother bird and this is a father bird. They both have openings under their tails. Eggs are inside the mother's opening, and sperm cells are inside the father's. Sperm cells look like tadpoles. But they are so tiny that they can be seen only with a microscope. In a way, they work like pollen.

"When the father bird puts his opening against the mother's, sperm cells enter her and swim to the egg. One reaches it first and joins with it. Then, a change occurs in the egg."

"*I* know!" exclaimed Laura. "The egg is fertilized."

"That's right," said Miss Florence, "and the fertilized egg begins to grow. Now it can become a baby bird."

"Is it a boy or a girl?" Sammy asked.

"That depends on the kind of sperm cell that joined the egg. Some sperm cells can make only boys, and others can make only girls.

"For one day , the fertilized egg stays inside the mother. A shell forms around it to protect it. Then it moves out of her through the same opening that the sperm went in.

"She sits on the egg in its shell to keep it warm. At first, the baby doesn't look like a bird at all. But after 6 days, it begins to. It has ears, eyes, and a beak. A sac with yolk is attached to its tummy. The yolk will be its first food.

"After seventeen days, the bird is big enough to live outside the shell. The sac of yolk pulls into its tummy, and the baby bird bangs its beak against the shell to break it open, and climbs out. That is how a baby bird is born," said Miss Florence.

Sammy's eyes opened very wide. He finally burst out, "Is my mommy going to sit on a shell, too?"

"No, Sammy. The baby is growing inside of her."

"But if she sat on it, I could almost tell what it's going to be like before it's born. I could feel it move. Why doesn't she sit on it?"

"Because the baby is fed and protected inside of her. But you know, you really should ask your mommy about it. She can tell you best of all."

The two children stared at each other in surprise.

"Why didn't we do that in the first place?" Laura exclaimed.

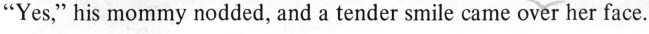

"Thank you," they called as they ran down the hill, past the mud castle that a squirrel was now perched on, over a bridge with a statue of a mermaid, over the picket fence around Sammy's house, and up to the porch where his mother was sitting.

"Mommy, mommy!" Sammy cried. "We were just on a search to find out where babies come from. We found out about flowers and birds, but not about people. Could you tell us?"

"Yes," his mommy nodded, and a tender smile came over her face.

She took them inside to a comfy armchair, and lifted her son onto her lap.

"Sammy," she said, "this baby was made the same way you were, and it is growing inside of me just the way you once did.

"At first, it was a tiny egg. It was in one of my ovaries. I have two ovaries and they are under my bellybutton. Hundreds of eggs are in them. Each month, an egg leaves only one ovary. But it cannot become a baby unless it is fertilized. When this egg left the ovary, it was fertilized by Daddy."

"Daddy has a penis between his legs. Under it is a bag of skin with two glands called testicles. Millions of tiny sperm cells are in these testicles.

"Daddy put his penis into an opening between my legs which is my vagina. Hundreds of sperm cells left him and traveled toward the egg. Many reached it, but only one joined with it. That sperm cell fertilized the egg.

"The fertilized egg then went to my uterus which is a muscular organ connected to my ovaries by two tubes. That's where it started to grow into a baby."

"How did it grow?" Laura asked.

"At first, it looked like a small dot — not like a baby at all. Soon after it was in my uterus, a bag of fluid formed around it to protect it."

"Won't it drown?" Laura asked, worried.

"No, because it does not breathe through its nose or lungs until it is born.

"In the bag, it kept on growing quickly. Its heart started beating when it was twenty-five days old. And at two months, it had tiny arms,

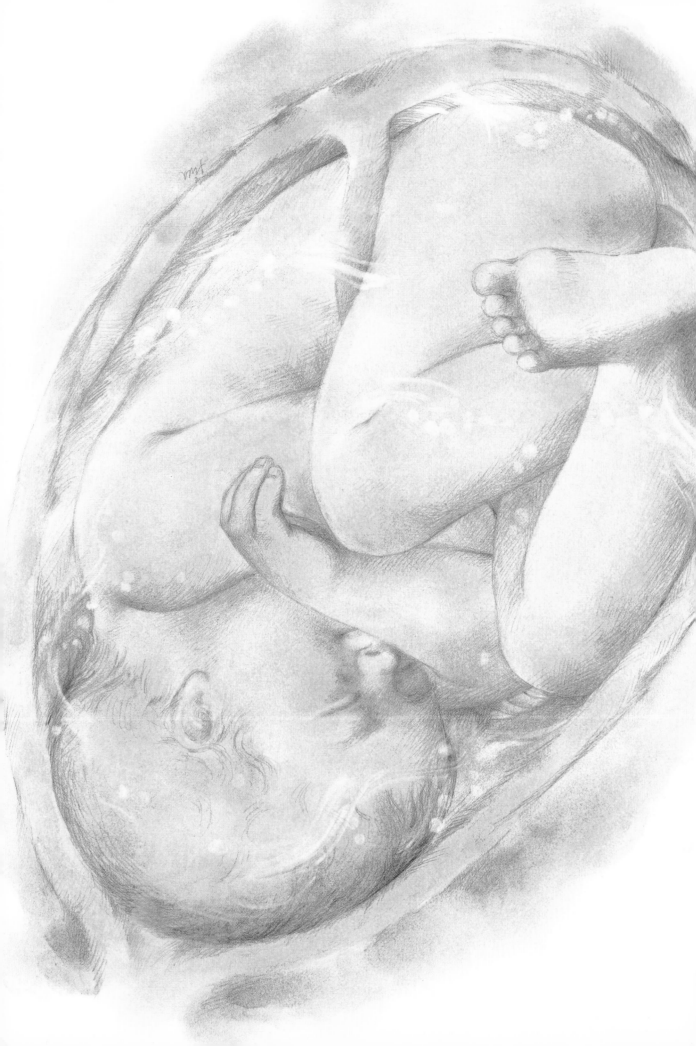

legs, and a head. Soon after, it had eyelids. But it couldn't open them."

"When can it?" Laura asked.

"Right about now," Sammy's mother said. "It has been growing for seven months, and it can open and close its eyes, kick its feet, and suck its thumb. It has hair and toes and fingernails, and looks just like a tiny baby."

"Is it hungry?" Sammy wanted to know.

"No, it's not hungry because it is getting fed. There is a cord connecting it to me. Blood flows through the cord bringing it food and air, too. So it's well nourished."

"Well, if it's so happy, why doesn't it stay inside of you forever?" Sammy blurted out.

"Because after nine months, it will be strong enough to live outside of me. It will be able to breathe by itself, and eat, too.

"A month before the baby is born, it will turn itself upside down. Then, when it is ready, the muscles in my uterus, which have held it tightly, will open up, and other muscles will push it out. The baby pushes itself too, and leaves my body through my vagina. The cord is still attached to it. A doctor cuts it off, but this doesn't hurt the baby or me. And that's how a baby is born."

"Mommy," Sammy murmured, "Will it be like me?"

"A little. But each person is special in his or her own way. Just like you are."

Two months passed quickly, and Sammy's mommy had a baby girl. Each day, Sammy and Laura spent a lot of time with the baby. They sang lullabies to her, hung a lace curtain around her crib, and even brought her a yellow toy duck.

One morning while Sammy's mommy was nursing, Laura thought back. "Wasn't that an exciting search we went on? We learned where all kinds of babies come from."

"Oh, that was okay," Sammy answered, "But a baby sister is something *really* super. Besides, I'm going to take her on some of the greatest searches ever. To find a treasure chest in a sunken pirate ship, a herd of galloping ponies, a field of four-leaf clovers, a lost city in the woods, and a pond of friendly salamanders and toads croaking in the night time. But I'll only take her if she's good."

THE END